Preface   iv

Acknowledgements   v

Executive summary   vi

1   Introduction   1
2   Background   2
3   Basis of the recovery approach   3
    3.1   History of recovery   3
    3.2   Defining recovery   3
    3.3   Themes in recovery   5
    3.4   The role of treatment in recovery   6
    3.5   Recovery terminology and associated concepts   7
    3.6   The evidence base for recovery   8

4   Policy, workforce change and recovery   10
    4.1   Government and workforce policies and reports   10
    4.2   Workforce planning   11
    4.3   Understanding and valuing difference   13
    4.4   User participation   14
    4.5   Recovery development in other countries   14

5   Measuring recovery   16
6   Examples of recovery in practice   17
7   Some ongoing debates about the recovery approach   22
8   Implications of adopting the recovery approach   24
    8.1   What are the next steps?   24

9   Conclusions   26

References   27

Appendix 1   35
Appendix 2: Contacts for services given as examples   36
of recovery in practice

Preface

'Recovery' is gaining prominence as a guiding principle for mental health services which has evolved from the lived experience of people who use services. It is a concept that has attracted considerable enthusiasm and hope in an area often characterised by disillusionment and defeat. It presents all of us involved in mental health services with the challenge and opportunity to work together and to integrate our various skills and experiences.

We are therefore pleased to present this joint position paper to you as a contribution to the recovery debate and its development, particularly within mental health services.

In this paper we set out the various positions about recovery and state our joint understanding of what recovery means and its implications for the future development of services. We hope that our collaboration indicates both how helpful the recovery approach can be to services across social care and health and how that wider context of self-directed care and participation is informed by recovery development in mental health services.

This overview offers an encouraging and challenging invitation to mental health professionals, people who use services and family members alike. It invites us to work together so as to build on good practice and current guidelines and make recovery an essential focus of our developing services. The hope and ambition of this paper is that the central significance of recovery can be progressively embraced as a guiding purpose that we can hold in common and through that, that recovery will become the common experience of those who use the services we provide.

Richard Humphries,
Chief Executive, Care
Services Improvement
Partnership (CSIP)

Professor Sheila Hollins,
President, Royal College of
Psychiatrists (RCPsych)

Bill Kilgallon,
Chief Executive,
Social Care Institute
for Excellence (SCIE)

A common purpose:
Recovery in future mental health services

Care Services Improvement Partnership (CSIP)
Royal College of Psychiatrists (RCPsych)
Social Care Institute for Excellence (SCIE)

First published in Great Britain in May 2007
by the Social Care Institute for Excellence

ISBN 978-1-904812-24-1

This report is available in print and online
www.scie.org.uk

Care Services Improvement Partnership (CSIP)
Room 8E 44
Quarry House
Quarry Hill
Leeds
LS2 7UE
Tel: 0113 2545127
www.csip.org.uk

Royal College of Psychiatrists (RCPsych)
17 Belgrave Square
London SW1X 8PG
Tel: 020 7235 2351
Fax: 020 7245 1231
www.rcpsych.ac.uk

Social Care Institute for Excellence
Goldings House
2 Hay's Lane
London SE1 2HB
tel 020 7089 6840
fax 020 7089 6841
textphone 020 7089 6893
www.scie.org.uk

Front cover photograph: kindly supplied by Glenn Roberts. The front cover image of prayer lamps is from the Sri Meenakshi Temple, Madurai, Tamil Nadu, India. It illustrates aarti, 'the auspicious lighting of lamps'. It has been chosen because it carries a wealth of connections and associations with people of all cultures who have created and sustained light, often in dark places, as a harbinger of hope and a symbol of reaching beyond our suffering and limitations.

Acknowledgements

This paper was overseen by a steering group of senior representatives from each of the three sponsoring organisations (Richard Humphries, Chief Executive Officer, CSIP, Professor Sheila Hollins, President, RCPsych and Bill Kilgallon, Chief Executive Officer, SCIE) that was chaired by Antony Sheehan, Director General, Health and Care Partnerships at the Department of Health. Responsibility for the commissioning, development and production of the paper was allocated to a small project group of senior staff/members of each organisation who were also full members of the steering group (Piers Allott, National Fellow for Recovery, CSIP, Dr Glenn Roberts, RCPsych and Patricia Kearney, SCIE). A commissioning brief was prepared and expressions of interest sought from a number of potential writers and the Social Perspectives Network (SPN) appointed as the 'writer' of a draft paper. The final paper was based on the draft prepared by SPN for the project group and eventually signed off by the steering group on 8 March 2007.

The SPN writers group was Jan Wallcraft (lead), Jerry Tew, Raza Griffiths and Vicky Nicholls.

Executive summary

This joint position paper is the result of a collaboration between the Care Services Improvement Partnership (CSIP), Royal College of Psychiatrists (RCPsych) and Social Care Institute for Excellence (SCIE). It is intended to make a positive and supportive contribution to the development of ideas, planning, service development and practice based on contemporary concepts of recovery. It is based on the core belief that adopting recovery as a guiding purpose for mental health services favours hope and creativity over disillusionment and defeat.

This paper sets the concept of recovery in the context of developing national and international practice and debate, seeking to explore definitions, together with the challenges and implications of adopting such an approach. These challenges include reconsidering some fundamental concepts such as what it means to be a service delivery organisation, a professional, a person who uses services or a family member and how we judge effective treatments and supports. This paper recognises that our services are at an early stage in developing a recovery orientation and that there is an associated need for a new research agenda to guide the way forward.

Recovery is seen as having at least three different meanings: as a spontaneous and natural process; as a response to effective treatments and as a way of growing with or despite continuing disability. The latter is largely the focus of this paper.

Contemporary understandings of recovery continue to recognise the complexity of suffering associated with severe mental health problems but that it is possible to live well despite any limitations caused by the disability or illness; and that it may be possible to reconceptualise otherwise wasteful and destructive experiences as a challenge with a potential for positive outcomes.

Concepts of recovery emphasise the value and uniqueness of each person and regard their different viewpoints and cultural perspectives as a resource.

The history of the recovery concept is reviewed, tracing it back to the late 18th and early 19th centuries in England and its re-emergence in the 1980s and 1990s in the US and New Zealand. A significant and growing number of developments in England and Wales are described, which are often governed and led by people who use services, who are able to provide an account of the benefits of a recovery approach. There are also examples of 'recovery in practice' with contact details from a wide variety of organisations from those governed and run by people who use services to statutory sector developments and commissioning.

Common themes in recovery include the pursuit of health and wellness; a shift of emphasis from pathology and morbidity to health and strengths; hope and belief in positive change; meaning and spiritual purpose of distress; service supports reconceived as mentoring not supervisory; identity explored as a cultural issue; social inclusion (housing, work, education, leisure); empowerment through information, role-change, self-care; awareness of positive language-use in framing the experience of illness; personal wisdom encouraged in professional practice; and creative risk-taking replacing overcautious risk assessment.

This statement is an invitation for us all to consider how the implications of recovery might be applied in each of our settings, recognising that individuals and organisations are inevitably starting from different points on their journeys.

1   Introduction

There is increasing national and international interest in the concept of 'recovery', particularly in the field of mental health and psychiatry. It is a concept that has attracted considerable enthusiasm and hope in an area often characterised by disillusionment and defeat. The present interest in recovery initially arose from the lived experiences of people with severe mental health problems. Since then professional bodies, health care agencies and governments have become increasingly interested in adopting recovery as the guiding principle for mental health policy, practice and services.

This position paper was jointly commissioned by the Care Services Improvement Partnership (CSIP), the Royal College of Psychiatrists (RCPsych) and the Social Care Institute for Excellence (SCIE), to provide a succinct account of the meaning of recovery, its underlying principles and implications. It is set in the context of current government policy for England and Wales, with reference to developments in other UK nations and international examples of research and practice. It acknowledges that engagement with a recovery orientation is a matter of open and continuing debate for professions and services, and is intended to provide timely support and orientation for that debate, by clarifying areas of agreement alongside contentious and under-researched issues in need of further investigation.

2 Background

Recovery is a small and ordinary word whose application to mental health care has generated three principle usages (Ralph and Corrigan, 2005). Recovery can firstly be considered as a spontaneous and natural event. Some who meet diagnostic criteria overcome their problems without intervention. Secondly, recovery is the intended consequence of the skilful use of the full range of effective treatments. Thirdly, the experience of personal recovery can occur in the context of continuing symptoms or disabilities. The first usage relates to resilience and robustness and is relatively poorly understood; the second is the focus of evidence-based practice and treatment guidelines; and the third is substantially the focus of this paper, which fundamentally is about recovery of hope and ambition for living full and purposeful lives whatever the circumstances.

Many concerns about engaging with a recovery approach arise from thinking that these different concepts are in competition with one another, whereas they are complementary and synergistic. This paper fully accepts the value of educative and preventative measures that aim to build resilience for individuals and communities (DH, 2007); it also assumes the value of effective treatment for which there is reliable evidence. However, there is little real knowledge of how to prevent severe mental health problems, and most current treatments are only partially effective. Adopting a recovery approach harnesses the value of current treatments but is directed at living with and beyond these continuing limitations.

An emphasis on personal recovery focuses on collaboration, partnership working and self-directed care, all of which lead to choice and control for people who use services, their families and other supporters. A recovery approach may therefore be applicable across a wide variety of client groups and connects with many of the ways in which cultures other than European approach health challenges. It is an approach that positively values different cultural understandings and as such can begin to fuse learning from our current UK population that includes European, Eastern and African worldviews to inform services for the 21st century.

This emphasis on recovery is fully consistent with current government policies in health and social care in England and Wales, including the White Paper, *Our health, our care, our say* (DH, 2006a) and the *Commissioning framework for health and well-being* (DH, 2007), *Joint guidance on the employment of consultant psychiatrists* (CSIP, 2005) and evidence-based clinical guidelines such as NICE 1 (2006) on schizophrenia and NICE/SCIE 42 (2006) on dementia; it is broadly applicable to people with all long-term conditions (DH, 2005a).

3 Basis of the recovery approach

3.1 History of recovery

Roberts and Wolfson (2006) date the origins of recovery-oriented practice to the Tuke family who established The Retreat in York at the turn of the 18th century. William Tuke, a Quaker and a lay reformer, set out to create a family-like healing and spiritual environment for members of the Society of Friends. The Tukes showed that moral or psychological forms of treatment in a work-oriented, peaceful and pleasant environment could replace physical restraint. John Perceval, in *A patient's account of his psychosis, 1830-1832* (1974), gave an early autobiographical account concerning what helped and hindered in treatment and recovery from psychosis. From the start, personal accounts, alongside more systematic analysis, have been important contributions to the literature on recovery. They highlight putting values into practice (Woodbridge and Fulford, 2004), being strongly influenced by what is personally meaningful, and being oriented around outcomes rather than inputs.

More recently, the recovery approach has emerged from the writings of people who used services in the 1980s in the US, and in the 1990s in the UK (Lovejoy, 1984; Chamberlin, 1988; Deegan, 1988; Leete, 1989; Unzicker, 1989; Coleman, 1999; Reeves, 1999). Many wrote about coping with symptoms, getting better, and regaining a satisfactory sense of personal identity that was not defined by illness experience. Deegan compared her recovery from schizophrenia with the recovery of her friend who had been paralysed by an accident. Both experienced anguish, despair and hopelessness. Eventually both learned to manage their difficulties and achieve meaningful goals. Deegan became a research psychologist, teacher and trainer and her friend qualified to work with other disabled people. A wide range of influential writers have greatly encouraged others with their personal accounts of illness and recovery, and include mental health professionals. Mike Shooter, the immediate past president of the Royal College of Psychiatrists (RCPsych) is one (Roberts and Wolfson, 2004), and Alistair Campbell, the Prime Minister's former director of communications and strategy, is another (Cantacuzino, 2002). The accumulated wisdom and witness from such personal accounts in many ways form the foundation of a recovery approach (Leibrich, 1999; Ridgeway, 2000).

3.2 Defining recovery

There is not yet a succinct or universally accepted definition of recovery. In ordinary speech, recovery is often equated with cure, a return to how things were before the illness or injury occurred, a process of getting back to normal, but by this definition few, if any, who experience severe mental illness recover (Whitwell, 2005). However, for severe mental health problems, and in reality all long-term conditions, outcomes are more complex and are described both by resolution of symptoms, impacts on life domains affected by illness, and growth and development of other valued life experiences. Some professional definitions of recovery distinguish between 'complete clinical recovery', with total absence of symptoms, and 'social recovery', which means the ability to live a more or less independent life even if symptoms remain. The current concept of recovery includes both of these but has moved from professional definitions towards self-definition, such that the concept and experience of personal recovery is not limited by the presence or absence of symptoms, and disabilities, nor the ongoing use of services. The concept of personal recovery pivots around considerations of how to live and how to live well in the context of long-term mental health conditions. How to develop a strong and satisfactory personal identity that is not defined by illness is a key issue, for example: 'just because you have a diagnosis of schizophrenia doesn't mean that you have to be a schizophrenic'. This way of thinking about recovery engages with the seemingly paradoxical assertion that you can *be* well even if you *have* a long-term illness, or as the Stanford University self-management course put it, 'Living a healthy life with chronic conditions' (Cooper and Clarke, 2005).

Thus recovery has been defined as, 'a deeply personal, unique process of changing one's attitudes, values, feelings, goals, skills and roles. It is a way of living a satisfying, hopeful, and contributing life even with limitations caused by the illness. Recovery involves the development of new meaning and purpose in one's life as one grows beyond the catastrophic effects of mental illness' (Anthony, 1993).

Based on her personal experience, Deegan (1988) defines recovery as, 'a process, a way of life, an attitude, and a way of approaching the day's challenges'. The recovery literature (Allott et al, 2002; Ralph and Corrigan, 2005) similarly describes being *in recovery* as an ongoing process, which involves gaining or regaining many aspects of life that are usually taken for granted, and may be lost or severely compromised by mental illness. Recovery may involve many stages, and inevitably setbacks and uncertainty, and has been described as, 'an uncharted, unpredictable, and personal journey' (Antony Sheehan, preface to the National Institute for Mental Health in England (NIHME) *Inspirations, a calendar of recovery*, 2002).

The American Psychiatric Association's position statement, 'endorsing and strongly affirming the application of the concept of recovery', gathered many of these viewpoints and emphasised that recovery-based practice is based on broad partnerships that seek to uphold hope and maximise quality of life:

> The concept of recovery emphasises a person's capacity to have hope and lead a meaningful life, and suggests that treatment can be guided by attention to life goals and ambitions. [The recovery approach] recognizes that patients often feel powerless or disenfranchised, that these feelings can interfere with initiation and maintenance of mental health and medical care, and that the best results come when patients feel that treatment decisions are made in ways that suit their cultural, spiritual, and personal ideals. [The recovery approach] focuses on wellness and resilience and encourages patients to participate actively in their care, particularly by enabling them to help define the goals of psychopharmacologic and psychosocial treatments.... The application of the concept of recovery requires a commitment to a broad range of necessary services and should not be used to justify a retraction of resources. (APA, 2005)

The issue of definition and personal redefinition, in particular from being chronically ill to 'in recovery', lies at the heart of a recovery-based approach to long-term conditions. The meanings that are attributed to experiences and the stories that are told about them assume a particular importance in confirming illness or supporting wellness. There is also a shift of emphasis from clinical and social recovery to personal recovery, as valued and defined by the individual.

Recovery is the process of regaining active control over one's life. This may involve discovering (or rediscovering) a positive sense of self, accepting and coping with the reality of any ongoing distress or disability (Faulkner and Layzell, 2000) finding meaning in one's experiences, resolving personal, social or relationship issues that may contribute to one's mental health difficulties, taking on satisfying and meaningful social roles, and calling on formal and/or informal systems of support as needed (Leibrich, 1999). Services can be an important aspect of recovery but the extent of the need for services will vary from one person to another. For some people, recovery may mean exiting from mental health services either permanently or for much of the time. For others it may mean continuing to receive ongoing forms of medical, personal or social support that enable people to get on with their lives.

3.3 Themes in recovery

Engaging with a move towards recovery-based practice takes in far wider considerations than familiar concerns about giving or receiving effective treatment. It is about engaging with the complexities of lived experience and seeking to constructively support an increased possibility of recovery outcomes. The recovery literature has arisen largely from personal experience with more recognisably scientific evaluation and theory following later, and although rich in personal meaning it remains light on systematic analysis. The dynamics and essential components of the recovery process have yet to be fully understood or evaluated but the process of recovery has been recurrently associated with a number of core themes (Deegan, 1988; Onken et al, 2002; Turner-Crowson and Wallcraft, 2002; Allott, 2005; Ralph and Corrigan, 2005; Roberts and Wolfson, 2006). Taken together, these themes do not so much define recovery as sketch out the map on which recovery journeys are lived, and suggest directions for research, evaluation and the development of recovery-based practice and services.

Key themes include the following:

1. Recovery is fundamentally about a set of values related to human living applied to the pursuit of health and wellness.
2. Recovery involves a shift of emphasis from pathology, illness and symptoms to health, strengths and wellness.
3. Hope is of central significance. If recovery is about one thing it is about the recovery of hope, without which it may not be possible to recover and that hope can arise from many sources, including being believed and believed in, and the example of peers.
4. Recovery involves a process of empowerment to regaining active control over one's life. This includes accessing useful information, developing confidence in negotiating choices and taking increasing personal responsibility through effective self-care, self-management and self-directed care.
5. Finding meaning in and valuing personal experience can be important, as is personal faith for which some will draw on religious or secular spirituality.

6. Recognising and respecting expertise in both parties of a helping relationship which recontextualises professional helpers as mentors, coaches, supporters, advocates and ambassadors.

7. Recovery approaches give positive value to cultural, religious, sexual and other forms of diversity as sources of identity and belonging.

8. Recovery is supported by resolving personal, social or relationship problems and both understanding and realistically coming to terms with ongoing illness or disability.

9. People do not recover in isolation. Recovery is closely associated with social inclusion and being able to take on meaningful and satisfying social roles in society and gaining access to mainstream services that support ordinary living such as housing, adequate personal finances, education and leisure facilities.

10. There is a pivotal need to discover (or rediscover) a positive sense of personal identity, separate from illness and disability.

11. The language used and the stories and meanings that are constructed around personal experience, conveyed in letters, reports and conversations, have great significance as mediators of recovery processes. These shared meanings either support a sense of hope and possibility or carry an additional weight of morbidity, inviting pessimism and chronicity.

12. Services are an important aspect of recovery but the value and need for services will vary from one person to another. For some people, recovery is equated with detaching from mental health services either permanently or for much of the time. For others, recovery may be associated with continuing to receive ongoing forms of medical, personal or social support that enable them to get on with their lives.

13. Treatment is important but its capacity to support recovery lies in the opportunity to arrive at treatment decisions through negotiation and collaboration and it being valued by the individual as one of many tools they choose to use.

14. The development of recovery-based services emphasises the personal qualities of staff as much as their formal qualifications, and seeks to cultivate their capacity for hope, creativity, care and compassion, imagination, acceptance, realism and resilience.

15. In order to support personal recovery, services need to move beyond the current preoccupations with risk avoidance and a narrow interpretation of evidence-based approaches towards working with constructive and creative risk-taking and what is personally meaningful to the individual and their family.

3.4 The role of treatment in recovery

It remains important that treatment decisions are guided by evidence, but given the very high rates of discontinuation of treatment, how such decisions are made may be as important as the decision itself. People in recovery speak clearly about the value of negotiation and collaboration concerning treatment decisions with the evidence of an individual's experience, of whether something works or not in practice, given priority over general beliefs of what should work. Treatment is thus recontextualised as one out of many tools that can support recovery.

Pat Deegan is widely accepted as one of the inspirational leads of the international recovery movement and based on her personal experience she gave a helpful orientation to the balance of continuing to accept support and treatment while being fully engaged in self-care and self-management (Deegan, 1996).

> My journey of recovery is still ongoing. I still struggle with symptoms, grieve the losses I have sustained.... I am also involved in self help and mutual support and still use professional services including medications, psychotherapy, and hospitals. However, I do not just take medications or go to the hospital. I have learned to use medications and to use the hospital. This is the active stance that is the hallmark of the recovery process.

Wallcraft (2005) has similarity stated that, 'Hospital services are part of recovery but only in so far as they provide an environment that enables people to regain their ability to control and manage their own lives'.

It is this shift from an entanglement or passive dependency on services to an 'active stance' of selectively, thoughtfully and positively using treatment and services to support independence and self-management that characterises journeys in recovery for people with long-term conditions. Clearly these views have implications for both those who use and those who provide such services.

3.5 Recovery terminology and associated concepts

Some people use terminology with similar or slightly different meanings from recovery. It is unhelpful to see these associated concepts as in competition with one another as the recovery concept can encompass all of these meanings, but is not restricted to any one of them:

- *Rehabilitation:* an organised statutory or voluntary sector programme designed to improve physical, mental, emotional and social skills to enable a transition back into society and the workplace.
- *Discovery:* taking a personal journey to new understandings of oneself and the world, rather than simply returning to the old self.
- *Restitution:* regaining some of what has been lost or taken away due to ill-health, for example, social status, contacts, self-esteem.
- *Self-care:* looking after oneself well.
- *Self-management:* making one's own health decisions and learning to manage long-term health problems, so as to live well with the minimum reliance on services.
- *Self-directed care:* being informed and having the ability to exercise choice and responsibility for care provided to you by others.
- *Coping strategies and strategies for living:* finding what helps one cope with problems and building one's own set of tools for dealing with mental or physical health problems.
- *Healing and wellness:* rediscovering one's inner capacity for self-healing, with or without help from a practitioner and achieving a state of well-being, even if some of the symptoms remain.
- *Resilience:* having the ability to survive and to learn from life's challenges.

- *Transformation:* a term used with respect to a process, outcome and vision for individuals and services that is not an end in itself but rather an intermediate state through which the goal of facilitating recovery in people's lives is realised.

3.6 The evidence base for recovery

Most research on the three principle usages of recovery has so far arisen from clinical perspectives that define rates of recovery in terms of symptomatic or socio-economic changes. However, as Dorrer (2006) observed, most such longitudinal outcome studies use objective measures of clinical and social recovery that may be blind to what is subjectively meaningful to individuals. Research reviews should be aware of this limitation and that to date most studies have focused on recovery from symptoms, disabilities and dependence on services rather than personally defined outcomes such as recovery of hope, identity and a life regarded by the individual as worth living.

However, even within clinically focused research the evidence shows that within that framework of meaning and evaluation a high proportion of people can and do recover. Much of the emphasis of longitudinal studies has been on psychotic conditions, in particular schizophrenia, but considerable hope has been drawn from finding both heterogeneity and unexpectedly high levels of recovery and improvement (50-70%) over lengthy periods (20-35 years) (Calabrese and Corrigan, 2005), leading to independent living, and in Harding et al's studies (1987), an absence of signs of schizophrenia. Current interest in recovery has prompted a re-emphasis of evidence for favourable outcomes and late recovery based on familiar clinical definitions as grounds for optimism and as a means of challenging the chronicity paradigm (Harrison et al, 2001).

Recovery rates for mental illnesses are noted to surpass the treatment success rates for many other physical illnesses, including heart disease (NAMHC, 1993). NAMHC states that recovery rates include: schizophrenia, 60%, bipolar disorder, 80%, major depression, 65-80%, and addiction treatment, 70%. The possibility that outcomes may depend on considerably more than effective treatment has been emphasised by Warner (1994), who traces the history of recovery from schizophrenia, analysing all the European and North American follow-up studies he could find, between 1880 and 1985. His thesis is that recovery is generally linked to productive and satisfying activity and to doctors' expectations; at times and places where doctors are more optimistic about the possibility of recovery, recovery rates appear to be higher.

There is an extensive literature exploring possible mediating factors in recovery, but the present emphasis on supporting personal recovery even in the context of continuing symptoms and disabilities offers many new opportunities for evaluative research. These in turn may depend on development and validation of new measures (see sections on 'Measuring recovery' and 'Implications') that understand the concept of recovery as having very broad applicability to many domains of life where people struggle with long-term conditions that may not be particularly responsive to treatment measures. This shifts from an exclusive focus on the problem, to the person struggling with and learning to cope with and manage the problem. Recovery is significantly about recovering an emphasis on the relationship people have with their problems as a counterweight to the endemic tendency to see people defined as and by their problems. Therefore a recovery approach is as relevant to seeking progress in the context of defined illnesses as it is with problems such as challenging behaviour in learning disability (Banks, 2007).

The extension from traditional to new models of recovery described in this paper brings with it new challenges in determining reliable methods of evaluation and in the creation of evidence. In order to develop an evidence base for personal recovery there will need to be significant developments in determining meaningful measures for individuals and service outcomes as well as progress in systematic analysis informing practice guidelines. See, for example, the new typology for systematic analysis of evidence in support of the *National Service Framework for long-term conditions* (DH, 2005a, annex 2), which 'reflects the value placed on the opinions of people who use services and their families/carers, as well as the views of professionals', and, 'is based on the principle that qualitative, quantitative and mixed studies can have equal validity when used in the appropriate context, rather than suggest there is an implicit hierarchy among research designs'. In addition, SCIE has completed work on types and quality of knowledge (SCIE, 2003) as well as guidelines on systematic reviews, and has commissioned a systematic review on recovery.

4 Policy, workforce change and recovery

4.1 Government and workforce policies and reports

New ways of thinking and working will only flourish in a sympathetic policy and funding context. This supports innovators and gives a rationale and resources to others to take up these new ideas and practices. In fact, the recovery approach is wholly congruent with the current direction of government health and social care policy.

1. The *National Service Framework for mental health* (DH, 1999) sets the basis for recovery in its emphasis on information, empowerment, partnership, community-based care, family support and health promotion. National Service Framework standards provide guidance on promoting mental health, wellness and social inclusion, better access to primary care, written secondary care plans and home treatment where possible. Carers and families are entitled to an assessment.
2. *The NHS Plan* (DH, 2000) builds on the National Service Framework by setting down the resources needed to support it, including crisis and home treatment teams and STR (support time and recovery) workers.
3. *Reaching out: An action plan on social exclusion* (Cabinet Office, 2006) is one of the most recent policy initiatives to recognise the links between mental illness and social exclusion and provide opportunities for developing recovery-based services.
4. *Creating a patient-led NHS* (DH, 2005b) focuses on choice of treatments and services, information, valuing people as individuals, race equality action, understanding local needs, patient preferences and improving patient and public involvement.
5. *Improving the life chances of disabled people* (Prime Minister's Strategy Unit, 2005) sets out a plan to ensure that by 2025 'disabled people in Britain should have full opportunities and choices to improve their quality of life, and will be respected and included as equal members of society'. The means used to move towards this include individual budgets, support to families and young people, and help to get and keep employment through support, training and benefit reforms.
6. *Our health, our care, our* say (DH, 2006a) supports a recovery approach across health and social care services. Primary Care Trusts (PCTs) will be expected to involve communities in decision making. There will be greater incentives for preventive care to focus more on maintaining wellness and healthy living, with improved coordination of social and health care, and more flexible access for patients. Empowerment should be aided by an expanded Expert Patient programme (DH, 2001c) and personal health and social care planning for long-term conditions. There will be greater support for carers and an updated national carers' strategy. The expansion of direct payments, self-directed care and individual budgets will support self-managed care, and there is a clear duty on statutory bodies to encourage and support participation.
7. *Supporting people with long-term conditions to self-care* (DH, 2006b) sets out the evidence base for the policy of self-care, showing that it can reduce the use of GP and hospital services and drug expenditure: 'Patients are the health service's biggest untapped resource ... services need redesigning so that patients and the public are truly partners and co-producers in their own care'. This has also led to a requirement that all Royal Colleges include training competencies in supporting self-care in their core curricula.

8. The cross-government initiative, *Putting people in control of their care* (DH, 2005c), led by the Department of Health with the Department for Work and Pensions and the Department of Communities and Local Government, is supporting 'In-Control' and the piloting of individual budgets and self-assessment including widening direct payments, in particular to groups that are currently excluded, and developing and piloting the concept of individual budgets

9. *Strong and prosperous communities*, the local government White Paper (DCLG, 2006), aims to give local people and local communities more influence and power to improve their lives. It is about creating strong, prosperous communities and delivering better public services through a rebalancing of the relationship between central government, local government and local people. The paper is intended to show confidence in local government, local communities and other local public service providers by giving them more freedom and powers to bring about the changes they want to see.

10. The *Commissioning framework for health and well-being* (DH, 2007a) means involving the local community to provide services that meet their needs, beyond just treating them when they are ill, but also keeping them healthy and independent. The framework builds on the White Paper *Our health, our care, our say*. It is for everyone who can contribute to promoting physical and mental health and well-being, including the business community, government regional offices and the third sector.

11. The recent progress report, *Mental health: New ways of working for everyone* (DH, 2007b) Clarifies implications for specific professions and emphasises the need to develop strong and capable teams which make the most of new roles such as Support Time and Recovery workers, and new forms of functional and flexible working. It powerfully reemphasises the value of developing a recovery orientation across the whole of mental health practice.

4.2 Workforce planning

Putting new ideas and policy into practice requires robust workforce development, and there is currently considerable activity around redefining the mental health workforce that incorporates recovery approaches. The report on workforce skills needed to implement the *National Service Framework for mental health* sets out *The ten essential shared capabilities* (Hope, 2004) and specifically includes promoting recovery. They are regarded as essential for all mental health professionals as a platform to equip and unite the workforce in the common purpose of promoting recovery. In addition to emphasising the need for the workforce as a whole to develop recovery skills, each of the traditional mental health professions has begun a process of considering how to develop practice and practitioners in ways that are consistent with an emphasis on recovery.

The integration of social workers into Mental Health Provider Trusts offers an opportunity for the development of the social model in mental health care. This is being carried forward through the New Ways of Working groups of the Workforce Development Programme. Social work has long-standing experience of person-centred approaches and participative working. Its working principles of empowerment and a rights base are reflected in the specific duties of the approved social worker (Mental Health Act 1983) and most recently expressed in the General Social Care Council *Codes of practice* (GSCC, 2002).

The British Psychological Society (2000) has begun to explore the implications of recovery thinking as it relates in particular to severe mental illness. The writers argue that since there is no complete understanding of the complex causes of mental illness, services should respect each individual's understanding of their own experiences and acknowledge people who use services as experts on their own experience.

A report on the employment of consultant psychiatrists (CSIP, 2005a) discusses the role for psychiatrists, in particular those who work in rehabilitation in promoting the recovery agenda:

> [They] will need to work in partnership with commissioning agencies to develop socially inclusive recovery services. These need to be developed with appropriate support services for families, and for work, education, social and leisure activities. Rehabilitation consultants ... work in services which should be focused on service users and which prioritise service user involvement. [They] are, therefore, ideally placed to promote the recovery ethos throughout local general mental health services through skills sharing, education and training.

In addition, RCPsych, along with all other medical Royal Colleges, is currently developing training competencies in supporting people in self-care for inclusion in its core curriculum. This is a direct response to guidance on changes in professional practice described in the White Paper *Our health, our care, our say*.

A recovery approach is consonant with the models that already form the core of occupational therapy theory and practice (College of Occupational Therapists, 2006). In 1967 Elizabeth Yerxa described the person as 'a unique individual whose very humanness entitles him to choices in determining his own destiny' (Creek, 1990). Hagedorn (2004) writes that the principle concerns of occupational therapy are 'to enable and empower people to be competent and confident performers in their lives and thereby to enhance wellbeing and minimise the effects of dysfunction and environmental barriers'.

Occupational therapists believe that, for the individual to achieve and realise their hopes, they must be seen as a whole person, in their entirety, and in order to reach their optimum level of recovery and well-being the choices must be made by the individual, and they ought not to be 'moulded' into a pre-determined lifestyle created by the therapist or any other person with whom the individual comes into contact. Thus the therapist will use 'directed purposeful occupations to encourage and enable the person to assume responsibility to meet his or her needs' (Reed and Sanderson, 1992).

From values to action (DH, 2006c) sets out the mental health nursing perspective on recovery:

> Mental health nursing should incorporate the broad principles of the Recovery Approach into every aspect of their practice. This means working towards aims that are meaningful to service users, being positive about change and promoting social inclusion for people who use mental health services, their families and other informal supporters.

And mental health nurses are already considering how to fulfil this guidance and create a form of practice that reconstructs the professional role substantially around supporting hope of recovery (Watkins, 2007).

Progressive developments in individual professions have been gathered together and reemphasised in the recent progress report on *New ways of working* (DH, 2007b). This gives considerable support for the whole mental health workforce growing in the direction of recovery oriented practice, and illustrates some of the implications for workforce planning and development.'

4.3 Understanding and valuing difference

All health and social care is required to be appropriately sensitive to cultural differences and gender-based values and experiences. These issues may have particular significance as mediating factors in recovery and deserve special consideration; they may also represent particular resources in support of recovery. Recovery can best be achieved in supportive environments of shared values, beliefs, spirituality (in a non-denominational sense) and ideologies, enabling sharing of narratives with people of one's own background and worldview. The support of families, including extended families and natural support systems, is particularly important to many people. Recovery needs to take account of individual differences and histories as well as social, ethnic, gender and sexual orientation. There can never be a 'one size fits all' approach and a recovery emphasis goes further than seeking equality concerning diversity in considering how these personal, familial, community and racial differences can be positively valued as a reservoir of meaning and identity that holds significant potential for self-definition and support for recovery processes. Being in touch with one's community and one's cultural roots and history helps good mental health.

New Zealand has engaged with and accounted for the specific cultural needs of people who use services within Maori communities and so has developed an approach that recognises the universal need for cultural identity and a sense of place and personal origins (Lapsley et al, 2002; Mental Health Commission, 2007).

However, there are also interesting and important tensions between different cultural perspectives represented within the recovery movement. The North American recovery literature has been criticised for an excessively individualistic approach that sidelines ethnicity and its social consequences for people who use services and 'projects traditional American values onto disabled people, such as rugged individualism, competition, personal achievement and self-sufficiency', and fails to appreciate that for some people who use services, independent living can be a lonely and isolated experience of living in a single room in a boarding house (Deegan, 1988). This contrasts with the New Zealand perspective (Fenton and Te Koutua, 2000; O'Hagen, 2001; Lapsley et al, 2002), which has illustrated the importance of valuing a person's cultural origins and personal meanings as reference points around which to support their citizenship and combat stigma. Recovery is then based on 'knowing who you are, and where you come from, and reintegrating yourself with your own people in your own way' (Lapsley et al, 2002).

Recovery also needs to take the particular needs and experiences of people with disabilities into account. People with learning disabilities are rarely included in the thinking around serious mental illness and recovery and are not greatly included in National Framework Strategies for mental health. However, 'person-centredness' is a key feature of learning disability policy and strategy (see DH, 2001a; Scottish Office, 2005). There are organisations such as Circles Network, which is a national voluntary organisation based around the key principles of inclusion and person-centred planning approaches. They provide unique personal support for people who are in danger of becoming socially excluded, or who are currently suffering the consequences of prior segregation and discrimination. They use the tools of person-centred planning to facilitate inclusion in the community, principally through the setting up of circles of support. The possibility of personal recovery in the context of persisting disabilities fully illustrates the paradoxical nature of recovery and its distinction from conventional concepts of cure.

4.4 User participation

The principles of user participation and the social model of care that complements them address wider issues than mental health recovery. However, participative approaches will enhance staff understanding and awareness of person-centred working and how this helps recovery services to be relevant to all people who use services (see DH, 2001b). In addition, participative research holds the possibility of not only accessing an intimate understanding of the dynamics of recovery but can itself be a support for recovery (Jacobson et al, 2005; Pitt et al, 2007).

4.5 Recovery development in other countries

The UK has much to learn from other countries, in particular New Zealand and the US. The Wisconsin Blue Ribbon Commission made recommendations that:

> The field should promote consumer-directed, family-supporting, outcome oriented, cost-effective service systems characterized by expectations of recovery, community integration, and an affirmative desire to fund only 'best practice' services; should engage consumer and family members throughout the workforce; *and should fund consumer and family-operated services.* (Wisconsin, 1997; emphasis added)

In recovery: The making of mental health policy by Nora Jacobson (2004) details the journey toward recovery for the mental health system in Wisconsin from 1999 to 2003. This account of the implementation of a policy of recovery will have some resonance for services in England since the system of 'functionalised services' established, particularly in Madison, inspired the system adopted within *The NHS Plan*.

The New Zealand Mental Health Commission (2001) produced a set of recovery competencies for workers, stating that a competent mental health worker:

- understands recovery principles;
- recognises and supports the personal resourcefulness of people with mental illness;

- accommodates diverse views of mental illness, treatments, services and recovery;
- understands and actively protects the rights of people who use services;
- understands discrimination and social exclusion, its impact on people who use services and how to reduce it;
- acknowledges the different cultures and how to work in partnership with them;
- has comprehensive knowledge of community services and resources and actively supports people who use services to use them;
- has knowledge of the 'service user' movement and is able to support its participation;
- has knowledge of family perspectives and is able to support their participation.

The US Substance Abuse and Mental Health Services Administration (SAMHSA) produced a *National consensus statement on mental health recovery* (SAMHSA, 2005) that opens with, 'Recovery is cited, within Transforming Mental Health Care in America, Federal Action Agenda: First Steps, as the "single most important goal" for the mental health service system'. It identifies the 10 fundamental components of recovery as being:

1. Self-direction
2. Individualised and person-centred
3. Empowerment
4. Holistic
5. Non-linear
6. Strengths-based
7. Peer support
8. Respect
9. Responsibility; and
10. Hope.

5 Measuring recovery

Putting recovery into practice and measuring recovery outcomes have been ongoing challenges, as noted in the section on 'The evidence base for recovery'.

In the US and the UK work has begun to develop measures of recovery that respond to personal perspectives and lived experience. Ralph et al (2000), updated by Campbell-Orde et al (2005), give measures developed in the US that include measurements of hope and empowerment as well as recovery.

One measure that is emerging as particularly relevant is DREEM (Developing Recovery-Enhancing Environments Measure) (Ridgway and Press, 2004; Allott et al, 2006). The National Institute for Mental Health in England (NIMHE) has identified DREEM as the most promising of an emerging group of recovery-sensitive measures (REE, in Campbell-Orde et al, 2005). DREEM provides a user-led structure that enables services to measure their commitment to, and effectiveness in, providing recovery-based care. It focuses on service development and enhances collaborative work with people who use services, thus mirroring the principles of the recovery it measures. A recent user-led evaluation used DREEM to find out how staff and residents in a recovery-oriented rehabilitation service in Devon rated 24 components of recovery, according to their importance. The team valued DREEM as providing a clear and structured model of recovery for staff and residents to use together to assess their service (Dinniss et al, 2007).

A number of writers, including Roberts (2000, 2006), have talked about the importance of narrative inquiry as a method of research, as well as a method of supporting recovery. Brown and Kandirikirira (2006) describe a recently completed study that examined over 60 recovery narratives in Scotland, to establish the factors that helped and hindered recovery, and highlighted helpful approaches to promote recovery narratives. Roberts (2000) argues for the importance of narrative, alongside and integrated with evidence-based medicine:

> Narrative is endemic to medicine, but has been excluded in the rise of EBM (evidence-based medicine). It remains to be seen whether narrative's ecumenicalism will be rebuffed or reconciled with EBM's fundamentalism, but there are signs of convergence.... There is an emerging image of the mature and experienced clinician of the future, who will have the capacity to integrate narrative- and evidence-based perspectives, quantitative and qualitative methods, and have a balanced awareness of the contributions and limitations of both as a sound basis for clinical judgements.

An agreed definition of recovery is needed, which can be operationalised into brief, reliable and valid measures, sensitive to multiple viewpoints and able to account for both personal changes and service outcomes. These measures will help to evaluate change and the impact of interventions but also contribute to a dynamic model of recovery itself and help to investigate mediating factors.

6 Examples of recovery in practice (contact details in Appendix 2)

A growing number of services are putting recovery into practice. Service models include Devon and Torbay, Hertfordshire, Northamptonshire, Powys, Scotland, Sefton Recovery Group Network (SRGN), South London and Maudsley (SLAM), Stockport and Stoke-on-Trent.

The Devon and Torbay Local Implementation Team (LIT) has committed itself to develop future services based on its recovery statement:

> Services will be delivered increasingly within mainstream primary and community settings. People who need services to be delivered in specialist facilities will be enabled to maintain and regain their health, wellbeing and support networks. These services will be based on the principles of recovery, self-help, early intervention, mainstream and social inclusion.

Recovery is led by Recovery Devon (Partnerships for Mental Health), an open group of people interested in promoting recovery-focused approaches and chaired by people with lived experience. A voluntary recovery strategy is being launched by the group with each team or organisation across statutory, voluntary and independent groups, setting and monitoring targets. Recovery awareness training is being rolled out across the Devon Partnership NHS Trust and induction for all staff will be set in a recovery context. One hundred and fifty STR workers are trained in recovery and wellness recovery action planning (WRAP) (Copeland, 1997, 2005), and service user volunteers are invited to complete the course. All social care contracts require recovery conditions of tender, and redesigned services are seeking to translate recovery theory into practice. A five-day intentional peer support course hopes to prepare 40 people with lived experience to disseminate and promote peer support skills. The website www.RecoveryDevon.co.uk is the communication channel for recovery developments.

A new **Centre for Mental Health Recovery** has been established at the University of Hertfordshire, the first such centre based in a higher education setting in the UK, whose joint aim, with people who use services and family members, is to develop and deliver effective measurable recovery training and education for people who use services and family members and for anyone providing mental health and substance misuse services. The centre will encourage research into the concept of recovery and work collaboratively with its local trust and other providers to promote recovery-oriented mental health services and evidence-based practices that seek to improve the outcomes for people with mental ill health.

Northamptonshire Healthcare NHS Trust has produced a booklet using the basic principles of recovery, with information about different treatments, self-management techniques, checklists and internet sources. This has now been developed into a workbook for recovery planning based on the principles of WRAP. Its main areas are:

- stability: self-assessment and daily planning
- identifying and working with strengths
- anticipation: recognising signs, taking action and crisis planning
- information on treatments: medication, talking therapies, complementary therapies
- supporting environment: sharing plans, rights and internet resources (Crisp, 2006).

Additionally, staff and user questionnaires, based on the DREEM tool and the Ohio Consumer Outcomes Initiative Self-Assessment tool (Ohio Department of Mental Health, 1996) are being used to establish a baseline for future monitoring and to raise workforce awareness of recovery. (The Ohio Mental Health Consumer Outcomes System is an ongoing endeavour to obtain outcome measures for people who are served by Ohio's public mental health system that is recovery-focused and enables people with mental health problems to contribute to their assessment using a self-assessment form as part of the assessment process.) Findings to date in Northamptonshire are that the workforce is strong in supporting the initial stages of recovery, defined as 'from crisis to stability', but needs to do more on supporting people in the next part of the journey toward realising goals, ambitions and opportunities.

A pilot project for providing individual peer support in primary care is also under way centred on stages 2 and 3 of the stepped care approach (NICE 23, 2004). Peer supporters will listen to people's stories, and through accessing information and using self-management techniques, support individuals to decide on the way they want to work towards their recovery. It is proposed that individual peer supporters will be part of wider health and well-being teams, which, while providing an enhanced primary care mental health service based on the principles of social inclusion, will also establish a supportive pathway for people to leave secondary care.

In **Powys** there has been an emphasis on the development of 'recovery-based practice'. Drawing on local, national and international stories of personal recovery, service development, tools and training have been evolving around five principles – movement from:

1. Despair to hope
2. Disconnectedness to connectedness
3. Other people's responsibility to personal responsibility
4. Alienation to discovery
5. A passive sense of self to an active sense of self.

Through the work of the Powys Equals Partnership, tools have been developed to create the 'language of hope' and, in particular, to create a framework for the inclusion of skills associated with acknowledged lived experience (ALE), within recruitment practice of statutory and voluntary organisations (for example, STR workers).

Day services, within the county, are developing their capacity to support personal recovery, based on a pilot, Active Lifestyles, in Welshpool, that draws on the themes above, and supports people to be more active in their own communities.

Underpinning this work a number of tools have been developed, including: 'Taking Control', a simple self-help tool; 'Filling the Glass', a tool that underpins the pathway to more active participation in service provision, development and planning; and 'Circles of Hope', a tool that addresses the tensions in recovery-based approaches for individual people, peer supporters, practitioners, managers, policy makers and commissioners.

A one-day training programme has been jointly developed (based on a three-day programme from Queensland, Australia), and piloted: 'Moving towards recovery-based practice: an integrated training programme'. This is currently being delivered to mental health teams across Powys, which include statutory and voluntary sector staff, peer supporters and carers.

In Newtown, recovery-based practice has 'leaked out' into services for drugs and alcohol, young people, Woman's Aid, and other groups, and joint work has begun on how to develop this further.

In **Scotland**, *Delivering for mental health* (Scottish Executive, 2006a) sets out targets and commitments for the development of mental health services in Scotland. The recent Scottish Mental Health Nursing Review (Scottish Executive, 2006b) commits the Scottish Recovery Network (SRN) to making recovery 'environment audit tools' available to mental health nurse leads, complemented by work with NHS Education Scotland to develop a recovery training framework for mental health nurses. As a result work is under way to adapt another developing recovery assessment tool known as Recovery-Oriented Practices Index (ROPI) (Mancini et al, 2006) to assess the extent to which practice is focused around the promotion of recovery.

Sefton Recovery Group Network (SRGN) have captured the strengths and talents of their 350+ members through the power of focusing on well-being and using WRAP. The SRGN approach is based on building family and community peer support to give the group more influence and power to 'take back control' and improve the lives of each member. They have drawn on available community tools to help take their work forward and enable all local areas tackle the challenges of the 21st century, for example, relating directly to their Health and Overview Scrutiny Committee. Through this relationship they aim to enhance their role in driving local democracy, innovation and priorities through inspiring health and well-being collaborations. They are working to drive up best practice spend on self-management and peer support to equip people with the tools and skills to self-manage their deemed serious and enduring mental illnesses rather than a simple reliance on secondary care 'mental illness' services.

Sefton citizens want to make a positive difference to their own lives and the lives of others and this approach is enabling integration and cohesion of one of the most disadvantaged groups in society. Working together they believe they can continue to improve their public services and the overall wellness of their community, an integral part of the local government White Paper (DCLG, 2006) and *Commissioning framework for health and well-being* (DH, 2007). Through their relationship with the Health and Overview Scrutiny Committee they have begun to tackle the complex cross-cutting theme of percentage of total 'mental illness' spend on peer-governed, peer-operated wellness networks by focusing on what really matters to their members.

South London and Maudsley (SLAM) Foundation Trust is using a combination of top-down and bottom-up strategies. In March 2007 the trust endorsed a social inclusion, rehabilitation and recovery strategy, which states 'Recovery is something the individual defines and experiences. A mental health service cannot make someone recover, though it can support the process. *The primary aim of SLAM in its work with service users is to support them in their recovery*'. In addition, several local initiatives are under way across the trust that have emerged due to local interest and enthusiasm. For example, a training programme in recovery has been provided to 60 staff in Croydon, which provided insights into key questions such as how to recognise a recovery-focused mental health service, how to identify change in a positive direction, and how to develop pro-recovery attitudes and values in staff during periods of organisational change. The training has now been funded for roll-out and evaluation across Lambeth and Southwark, and is intended to contribute to changing the culture of services within SLAM.

Stockport Metropolitan Borough Council PCT and **Pennine Care Mental Health Trust**, drawing on the experience and drive of people using services and their carers, are redesigning their mental health provision using a recovery and social inclusion philosophy (Rethink, 2005). The Stockport Well-being Centre offers a social inclusion 'hub', a location for gathering information necessary for recovery, and 'spokes' – pathways reaching out into community networks. The centre provides a pool of expertise and resources to assist all the people of Stockport experiencing mental distress to maintain and improve their mental well-being as well as the town centre location promoting mental health awareness issues to the wider public.

The **Stoke-on-Trent Modernisation Board (LIT)** adopted a vision and values document in 2002. Their agreed core values relate to:

1. A mental health service that is based on person-centred recovery.
2. Including people into their community, not into the service system.
3. User-directed services.
4. Supporting the family and peer networks of the individual service user.
5. Valuing diversity.
6. Independence, well-being and choice partnerships.
7. Holistic services of care and intervention based in recovery.
8. Listening to service users.
9. Listening to, engaging and supporting carers.

A mental health service based on person-centred recovery means one that is focused on the needs of the person rather than being service-led. It is aimed at enabling each person who is experiencing mental distress to recover the fullest control of their own life and to achieve their hopes and full potential.

'User-directed services' means that mental health services promote more effective recovery through greater understanding of the experiences of people who use services and their family members (of disability, of recovery and of service delivery).

This requires positive efforts to hear their experiences and aspirations and translate these experiences into service design, planning, commissioning and delivery. People who use services and their family members will be involved in the planning, commissioning and implementation of services.

The LIT states that gaps and conflicts are particularly relevant where there is disparity in the level and quality of services across age groups and where there are transitional issues with regard to children's services and services for older adults. While the core values have been developed within adult mental health services they should be equally applicable to mental health services for all ages.

7 Some ongoing debates about the recovery approach

Genuine growth and development of recovery-based practice and practitioners depends on honest and open discussion that acknowledges difference and disagreement but is centred on the search for common objectives and a collaborative way forward (Topor, 2001; Jacobson, 2004). It is important, therefore, for this position paper to set out some of the concerns about the concept of recovery held by people who use services and of professionals.

Some professionals fear that promoting the hope of recovery for everyone with severe mental illnesses is false and unrealistic, and colludes with denial of illness. This problem may be based on a misunderstanding that arises from equating recovery with cure, rather than the broad conceptualisation of personal recovery described in this paper. However, proponents of recovery will need to consider whether there are limits to the application of a recovery approach and to account fully for the implications of a recovery orientation in situations of steady deterioration or tragic outcomes. In support of the view that there should be no 'recovery free zones' there are already interest groups working on the application of recovery principles in dementia, severe learning disability and forensic services.

People who use services can also misuse the concept of recovery or feel threatened by it. Some people who use services say that it is sometimes useful to appear to be 'recovered' to get out of the system even though they have not recovered in any meaningful sense. Some are concerned that the adoption of the recovery approach will lead to services being taken away, or that they will be pressured into taking unsuitable jobs. Some do not believe they will be able to recover, and are concerned that the recovery approach may threaten their established coping strategies (BME Focus Group, 2006).

People who use services are often concerned that if the recovery approach is adopted by mental health services, the person-centred and empowering aspects could be lost, and existing services be merely re-labelled as recovery services (BME Focus Group, 2006). For example Endersby (2007) raised concern about the risk of professionalising recovery that she described from her experience as:

> ... a unique individual personal experience and pathway which a person walks, with professional services (when needed) by their side. Their role is supportive not prescriptive, recovery is not a treatment. Any level of recovery comes from and begins within the person who takes that first step towards regaining their confidence. Services must accept and acknowledge the vital importance of this, and work together with us, it is our recovery process.

However, it is central to recovery services to be respectful of self-defined goals in recovery and to fully support self-care, self-management and self-directed care although as yet there is little experience or guidance on good practice.

There is a debate around uncertainty on the part of people who use services who think that recovery is what services deliver to them, and that this does not involve their personal responsibility. This is closely linked to reconsideration of what role professionals play in supporting recovery and a move from being experts who know what others should do to mentors and coaches that are able to support people discovering for themselves.

There is also a debate about recovery approaches bridging conventional divisions between people who use services and staff, such that there is an acknowledgement of the applicability of recovery to both those who provide as well as those who receive services. Many staff who have become interested are motivated to do such work because of their personal or family experience of mental health problems, although this is rarely acknowledged. Valuing 'lived experience' and being more open about such 'personal qualifications' may be a new and uncomfortable relationship for some professionals and people who use services, but holds great potential in dismantling unhelpful and over-defined differences between people who use and people who provide mental health services.

Wesley Sowers, President of the American Association of Community Psychiatrists (2007), states that 'we all have something to recover from, whether it is mental illness, addiction, physical disability, loss of loved ones, victimization or loneliness', 'for change to occur, we must first recognise what we need to change' and 'Recovery creates a community that all can take part in as it erases the distinctions of position, age, skin colour, religion, language, and education and joins us in our common humanity'. He says that, 'If we fail to recognise this capacity for recovery to unite us, we will have squandered a great opportunity to integrate our highly fragmented and siloed service systems'.

8 Implications of adopting the recovery approach

This position paper does not offer an end point but more a place to start from. It would be premature for this overview to give a detailed list of implications for its joint authors and the adjacent health care constituencies. Such an approach, offering a checklist or targets, would also be somewhat dissonant with 'a recovery-based approach', which emphasises collaborative working and the value of those involved taking responsibility for working out actions, implications and consequences at a more local and personal level.

We have brought together the guiding hopes, values, principles and opportunities that characterise a recovery emphasis and anticipate that a future review will be able to comment on how this has been developed in practice. This paper is therefore offered as an authoritative summary of the national and international discussion on recovery that began with the hopes and dissatisfactions of people using services and is progressively being accepted as a key organising principle with which to develop better services for the future.

The major implication of this paper is to understand and accept that there are major implications, and for each care constituency, group, faculty, discipline, or organisation to consider creatively engaging with working out what those implications may be in practice.

There is a debate to be had about the breadth of recovery. Is this an approach that can apply to the whole of health and social care? Can it influence the recovery of organisations? Could it significantly contribute to the rehumanising of mental health services and implementation of person-led and user-centred approaches? Is it a philosophy, concept and set of values that can unite people working for mental health in a common goal? We suggest the following as some of the issues that are in need of clarification and development:

* definition
* meaningful measurement of recovery for both individuals and services
* understanding mediating factors in recovery and chronicity
* the development of clear models and materials to support recovery-based practice and practitioners
* research on successful methods of supporting self-management
* the role and contribution of experts by experience and peer support
* guidelines for commissioning recovery-based services
* quality indicators for recovery-based services
* consideration of recovery-based approaches to public health education.

8.1 What are the next steps?

A recovery-based approach to mental health problems, treatments, supports and services carries wide implications that need to be thought through at every level. Guidance and suggestions concerning suitable next steps depend entirely on where an individual, profession, service or organisation is starting from. The most important step may be making a commitment to developing services and practice in a recovery-based way and reflecting on what might be some of the early stages in that development. Organisations may wish to consider setting up working groups to respond to this paper and access valued source materials (Appendix 1) so as to develop a clear strategy for local development. Some helpful aspects to consider include the following:

- Professions and services engaging with the overview offered in this paper and seeking to apply it to their own disciplines and circumstances.
- The implications for direct work with people who use services to raise their awareness and with it the possibility of their commitment to active engagement in their own recovery.
- The influence of the social model of care, as seen across the whole of health care as it becomes more focused on independence, rights, choice, empowerment and inclusiveness, which are key areas in the recovery approach. A better awareness of what people with severe mental health problems find most important to them puts mental health practice firmly on a recovery footing.
- Integrating a core emphasis on recovery into basic and postgraduate training, examination, supervision, appraisal, new ways of working, leadership and governance for the whole mental health workforce.
- Alongside a traditional emphasis on understanding psychopathology and treatment, the application of recovery values to teaching and learning in mental health would suggest: progressively involving experts by experience as trainers (a mandatory requirement in the training of psychiatrists); the importance of intentional peer support (Mead, 2005); the significance of narrative perspectives; self-management and self-directed care; and how mental health staff, people who use services and carers can work collaboratively to optimise recovery possibilities.
- A new research agenda could be formulated that takes in not only topics about recovery but also collaborative methods that are supportive of recovery.
- Recovery principles should underpin policy and practice. Policy and procedure manuals should prioritise self-directed care, self-management and recovery planning.
- Good practice should be identified and good practice examples disseminated.
- Opportunities should be taken to consolidate recovery practice through incorporation in NICE guidelines, SCIE Knowledge Reviews and Guides and in routine inspection standards (for example, Quality and Outcomes frameworks, Healthcare Commission Inspections, Commission for Social Care Inspections), although all would again be dependant on clarification of definition and measurement.

9   Conclusions

This joint position paper has reviewed the meaning, application and implications of a contemporary understanding of recovery. It holds a sense of hope and opportunity for the development of recovery-based practice across a wide range of health and social care services. It also identifies some of the associated challenges. Adopting a core emphasis on recovery involves a redefinition of what it means to have a long-term condition, and a revisioning of how services work with people with persistent symptoms and disabilities. It offers a challenge to some fundamental concepts such as what it means to be a service delivery organisation, a professional, a person who uses services or a family member, and how we judge effective treatments and supports. It broadens our understanding to consolidate the significance of values such as hope, respect and optimism alongside evidence.

This carries far-reaching implications for training, supervision, governance and service design. It anticipates a future when earlier hopes of effective community services will be realised, based on a sound understanding of how to support people in self-care, self-management and self-directed care, and holds hope for people with severe and long-term conditions being much more able to be in control of their own lives.

A recovery emphasis is not without its detractors and there are those who consider it as either naively unrealistic or based on linguistic and conceptual distortions. There are also some who worry about power and ownership. But there is considerable value in engaging with these difficulties and objections in the service of continued clarification, elaboration and focused research. Recovery is of no value if it is not authentic and both intellectually and clinically robust. There is a particular need to work out the implications of recovery thinking in the most difficult of circumstances, where choice and responsibility may be most compromised.

A core emphasis on recovery is already finding wide acceptance, providing a clear sense of direction, ambition and guiding purpose for services and organisations that seek to improve the mental health of individuals and communities. It is already being adopted by many people who use services and user-led groups as an inherently collaborative concept that provides a common aspiration and goal for better outcomes and better lives. It has provided a means of drawing into alliance people who use services and those who provide them. There are many good beginnings but still much to learn.

Finally, it is a widely accepted 'recovery competence' that in order to provide effective recovery services staff and service organisations need to attend to their own hope and morale. Both hope and despair are contagious and for the first time we are considering guiding principles and values for our work that emphasise that the health and well-being of the practitioner, and their organisation are a prerequisite for effective practice. We therefore commend this paper to your consideration and invite its acceptance and use as a stimulus to thinking through the implications of adopting a core commitment and orientation towards recovery in many diverse settings. We believe that to do so could significantly benefit those who use our services, their informal supporters, ourselves as practitioners, the organisations for which we work, and the communities in which we live and work, as well as our wider society.

References

Allott, P. (2005) 'Recovery', in D. Sallah and M. Clark (eds) *Research and development in mental health: Theory, framework and models*, Oxford: Elsevier Science Ltd.

Allott, P., Clark, M. and Slade, M. (2006) *Taking DREEM forward: Background and summary of experience with REE/DREEM so far and recommendations*, Report prepared for Director of Mental Health Research, Department of Health, available from authors at mentalhealthrecovery@blueyonder.co.uk

Allott, P., Loganathan, L. and Fulford, K.W.M. (2002) 'Discovering hope for recovery from a British perspective', International Innovations in Community Mental Health (Special Issue) (eds S. Lurie, M. McCubbin and B. Dallaire), *Canadian Journal of Community Mental Health*, vol 21, no 3.

Anthony, W.A. (1993) 'Recovery from mental illness: the guiding vision of the mental health service system in the 1990s', *Psychosocial Rehabilitation Journal*, vol 16, no 4, pp 11-23.

APA (American Psychiatric Association) (2005) *Use of the concept of recovery: Position statement* (www.psych.org/edu/other_res/lib_archives/archives/200504.pdf).

Banks, R. (2007) Personal communication received as commentary from the e-advisory group.

BME Focus Group (2006) Focus group on recovery run by the Social Perspectives Network as part of the drafting of the position paper.

British Psychological Society, The (2000) *Recent advances in understanding mental illness and psychotic experiences*, Leicester: Division of Clinical Psychology, The British Psychological Society.

Brown, W. and Kandirikirira, N. (2006) *Recovering mental health in Scotland. Report on narrative investigation of mental health recovery*, Glasgow: Scottish Recovery Network.

Cabinet Office (2006) *Reaching out: An action plan on social exclusion* (www.cabinetoffice.gov.uk/social_exclusion_task_force/publications/reaching_out/).

Calabrese, J.D. and Corrigan, P.W. (2005) 'Beyond dementia Praecox: findings from long-term follow-up studies of schizophrenia', in R. Ralph and P. Corrigan (eds) *Recovery in mental illness: Broadening our understanding of wellness*, Washington, DC: American Psychological Association, chapter 3.

Campbell-Orde, T., Chamberlin, J., Carpenter, J. and Leff, H.S. (2005) *Measuring the promise: A compendium of recovery measures, Volume II: The Evaluation Centre at HSRI* (www.tecathsri.org/product_description.asp?pid=129).

Cantacuzino, M. (2002) 'Coming back from the brink', *Sunday Times Magazine*, 6 January, p 38.

Chamberlin, J. (1988) *On our own*, London: Mind Publications.

Coleman, R. (1999) *Recovery: An alien concept*, Gloucester: Handsell Publishing (www.workingtorecovery.co.uk/Default.aspx?tabid=1056&CategoryID=1&List=0&Level=1&ProductID=19).

Cooper, J.M. and Clarke, A. (2005) *Expert patients: Who are they? Lay led self-management programmes: An additional resource in the management of chronic illness*, London: Long-term Medical Conditions Alliance, www.lmca.org.uk/docs/article.htm

Copeland, M.E. (1997) *WRAP – Wellness Action Recovery Planning* (www.mentalhealthrecovery.com).

Copeland, M.E. (2005) *WRAP – Wellness Action Recovery Planning* (UK ed P. Allott), Liverpool: Sefton Recovery Group Network (www.seftonrecoverygroup.org.uk/).

Creek, J. (ed) (1990) *Occupational therapy and mental health; Principles, skills and practice*, Edinburgh: Churchill Livingstone.

Crisp, T. (2006) *Into recovery: A workbook for recovery planning*, Northampton: Northamptonshire Healthcare NHS Trust.

CSIP (Care Services Improvement Partnership) (2005a) *Joint guidance on employment of consultant psychiatrists* (http://kc.nimhe.org.uk/upload/271394%20consultpsych1.pdf).

DCLG (Department of Communities and Local Government) (2006) *Strong and prosperous communities*, Local government White Paper, London: The Stationery Office.

Deegan,. E. (1988) 'Recovery: the lived experience of rehabilitation', *Psychosocial Rehabilitation Journal*, vol 11, pp 11-19.

Deegan, P. (1996) 'Recovery as a journey of the heart', *Psychiatric Rehabilitation Journal*, vol 19, no 3, pp 91-7.

DH (Department of Health) (1999) *National Service Framework for mental health: Modern standards and service models* (www.dh.gov.uk/PublicationsAndStatistics/Publications/PublicationsPolicyAndGuidance/PublicationsPolicyAndGuidanceArticle/fs/en?CONTENT_ID=4009598&chk=jmAMLk).

DH (2000) The *NHS Plan: A plan for investment, a plan for reform*, Cm 4818-1, London: The Stationery Office (www.nhsia.nhs.uk/nhsplan/).

DH (2001a) *Valuing People: A new strategy for learning disability for the 21st century*, Cm 5086 (www.archive.official-documents.co.uk/document/cm50/5086/5086.htm).

DH (2001b) *Nothing about us without us* (www.dh.gov.uk/en/ Publicationsandstatistics/Publications/PublicationsPolicyAndGuidance/DH_ 4006200).

DH (2001c) *The Expert Patient: A new approach to chronic disease management for the 21st century*, London: DH (www.ohn.gov.uk/ohn/people/expert.htm).

DH (2005a) *The National Service Framework for long-term conditions – Annex* (www. dh.gov.uk/assetRoot/04/10/57/80/04105780.pdf).

DH (2005b) *Creating a patient-led NHS* (www.dh.gov.uk).

DH (2005c) *Putting people in control of their care* (www.dh.gov.uk/NewsHome/ NewsArticle/fs/en?CONTENT_ID=4123522&chk=fkT8TM).

DH (2006a) *Our health, our care, our say*, London: The Stationery Office (www.dh.gov.uk/PolicyAndGuidance/OrganisationPolicy/Modernisation/ OurHealthOurCareOurSay/fs/en).

DH (2006b) *Supporting people with long-term conditions to self-care: A guide to developing local strategies and good practice* (www.dh.gov.uk/ PublicationsAndStatistics/Publications/PublicationsPolicyAndGuidance/ PublicationsPolicyAndGuidanceArticle/fs/en?CONTENT_ID=4130725&chk=o9VokD).

DH (2006c) *From values to action: The Chief Nursing Officer review of mental health nursing* (www.dh.gov.uk/CNO).

DH (2007) *Commissioning framework for health and well-being* (www.dh.gov.uk/en/ Publicationsandstatistics/Publications/PublicationsPolicyAndGuidance/DH_072604).

DH (2007b) *Mental health: New ways of working for everyone*, Progress report (www. google.co.uk/search?hl=en&q=Mental+Health%3A+New+ways+of+Working+ for+Everyone&btnG=Google+Search&meta=cr%3DcountryUK%7CcountryGB).

Dinnis, S., Roberts, G., Hubbard, C., Hounsell, J. and Webb, R. (2007) 'User-led assessment of the recovery orientation of a rehabilitation services using DREEM', *Psychiatric Bulletin*, vol 31, pp 124-127.

Dorrer, N. (2006) *Evidence of recovery: The 'ups' and 'downs' of longitudinal outcome studies*, SRN Discussion Paper Series, Report no 4, Glasgow: Scottish Recovery Network (www.scottishrecovery.net/content/mediaassets/doc/SRN%20Discussion %20Paper%204%20Outcomes.pdf).

Endersby, M. (2007) Personal communication received as commentary from the e-advisory group.

Faulkner, A. and Layzell, S. (2000) *Strategies for living: A report of user-led research into people's strategies for living with mental distress*, London: Mental Health Foundation.

Fenton, L. and Te Koutua, T.W. (2000) *Four Maori korero about their experiences of mental illness*, Recovery Series 1, Wellington: Mental Health Commission (www.mhc.govt.nz/publications/2000/Recovery_Maori.pdf).

GSCC (General Social Care Council) (2002) *Code of practice for social care workers and Code of practice for employers of social care workers* (www.gscc.org.uk/Good+practice+and+conduct/Get+copies+of+our+codes/).

Hagedorn, R. (2001) *Foundations for practice in occupational therapy* (3rd edn), Edinburgh: Churchill Edinburgh.

Harding, C.M., Brooks, G.W., Ashikaga, T., Strauss, J.S. and Breier, A. (1987) 'The Vermont longitudinal study of persons with severe mental illness, I: methodology, study sample, and overall status 32 years later', *American Journal of Psychiatry*, June, vol 144, no 6, pp 718-26.

Harrison, G., Hopper, K., Craig, T., Laska, E., Siegel, C., Wanderling, J., Dube, K.C., Ganev, K., Giel, R., An Der Heiden, W., Holmberg, S.K., Janca, A., Lee, P.W.H., León, C.A., Malhotra, S., Marsella, A.J., Nakane, Y., Sartorius, N., Shen, Y., Skoda, C., Thara, R., Tsirkin, S.J., Varma, V.K., Walsh, D. and Wiersma, D. (2001) 'Recovery from psychotic illness: a 15- and 25-year international follow-up study', *British Journal of Psychiatry*, vol 178, pp 506-17.

Hope, R. (2004) *The ten essential shared capabilities: A framework for the whole of the mental health workforce*, London: Department of Health and Sainsbury Centre for Medical Health (www.scmh.org.uk/80256FBD004F6342/vWeb/pcPCHN6FRLDM).

Jacobson, N. (2004) *In recovery: The making of mental health policy*, Nashville, TN: Vanderbilt University Press; see also *In recovery: 2 synopses* (www.journeyofrecovery.co.uk/Documents/2SynopsesCSIPFinal.pdf).

Jacobson, N., Altenberg, J., Barnes, J., Cusson, R., Rowley, V. and McKinnon, B. (2005) 'Recovery in community: Using participatory action research to explore recovery with alternatives', *Canadian Journal of Community Mental Health*, vol 24, no 2, pp 85-97.

Lapsley, H., Waimarie, L.N. and Black, R. (2002) *'Kia Mauri Tau!': Narratives of recovery from disabling mental health problems*, Wellington: Mental Health Commission (www.mhc.govt.nz/publications/2002/Kia_Mauri_Tau.pdf).

Leete, E. (1989) 'How I perceive and manage my illness', *Schizophrenia Bulletin*, vol 15, pp 197-200 (www.eastcommunity.org/shop/images/EssoLeete.pdf).

Leibrich, J. (1999) *A gift of stories: Discovering how to deal with mental illness*, New Zealand: University of Otago Press.

Lovejoy, M. (1984) 'Recovery from schizophrenia – a personal odyssey', *Hospital and Community Psychiatry*, vol 35, no 8, pp 809-12.

Mancini, A., Finnerty, M., Dornan, D. and Felton, C. (2006) *Defining and measuring principles for recovery-oriented care in mental health organizations*, New York, NY: New York State Office of Mental Health (www.nri-inc.org/conferences/Presentations/2006/SunMancini.pdf).

Mead, S. (2005) *Intentional peer support: An alternative approach*, Plainfield, NH: Shery Mead Consulting (www.mentalhealthpeers.com).

Mental Health Act 1983 (c 20), London: HMSO.

Mental Health Commission (2007) *Te Haererenga mo te Whakaoranga 1996-2006: The journey of recovery for the New Zealand mental health sector*, Wellington: Mental Health Commission (www.mhc.govt.nz/publications/2007/te-haererenga.pdf).

NAMHC (National Advisory Mental Health Council) (1993) 'Health care reform for Americans with severe mental illnesses', *American Journal of Psychiatry*, vol 150, pp 1447-65.

NICE 1 (National Institute for Clinical Excellence) (2006) *Guidance on schizophrenia: Full national clinical guideline on core interventions in primary and secondary care*, London: NICE (www.nice.org.uk/guidance/CG1/guidance/pdf/English).

NICE 23 (2004) *Depression: Management of depression in primary and secondary care* (www.nice.org.uk/pdf/CG023NICEguideline.pdf).

NICE/SCIE 42 (Social Care Institute for Excellence) (2006) *Guidance on dementia: Supporting people with dementia and their carers in health and social care*, London: NICE (www.nice.org.uk/guidance/cg42/niceguidance/pdf/English).

NIMHE (National Institute for Mental Health in England) (2002) *Inspirations, a calendar celebrating recovery*.

NIMHE (National Institute for Mental Health in England) (2005) *NIMHE guiding statement on recovery* (kc.nimhe.org.uk/upload/Recovery%Guiding%20Statement.pdf).

New Zealand Mental Health Commission (2001) *Mental health recovery competencies teaching resource kit*, New Zealand: Mental Health Commission (email: info@mhc.govt.nz).

O'Hagen, M. (2001) *Recovery competencies for New Zealand mental health workers*, Wellington: Mental Health Commission (www.mhc.govt.nz/publications/2001/Recovery_Competencies.pdf).

College of Occupational Therapists (2006) *Recovering ordinary lives: The strategy for occupational therapy in mental health services 2007-2017*, Literature review. (Core.) London: College of Occupational Therapists (www.cot.org.uk/members/publications/list/intro/pdf/RecovOL-Lit_ft.pdf).

Ohio Department of Mental Health (1996) 'Outcomes' (www.mh.state.oh.us/oper/outcomes/outcomes.index.html).

Onken, S.J., Dumont, J.M., Ridgway, P., Dornan, D.H. and Ralph, R.O. (2002) *Mental health recovery: What helps and what hinders? A national research project for the development of recovery facilitating system performance indicators*, Alexandria, VA: NTAC (National Technical Assistance Center) (www.nasmhpd.org/general_files/publications/ntac_pubs/reports/MHSIPReport.pdf).

Perceval, J. (1974) in G. Bateson (ed) *Perceval's narrative: A patient's account of his psychosis, 1830-1832*, New York, NY: William Morrow & Co Inc.

Pitt, L., Kilbride, M., Nothard, S., Welford, M. and Morrison, A. (2007) 'Researching Recovery from psychosis: a user-led project', *Psychiatric Bulletin*, vol 31, pp 55-60.

Prime Minister's Strategy Unit (2005) *Improving the life chances of disabled people* (www.cabinetoffice.gov.uk/strategy/work_areas/disability/).

Ralph, R. and Corrigan, P. (eds) (2005) *Recovery in mental illness: Broadening our understanding of wellness*, Washington, DC: American Psychological Association.

Ralph, R.O., Kidder, K. and Phillips, D. (2000) *Can we measure recovery? A compendium of recovery and recovery-related instruments*, Maine, MD: Center for Mental Health Services, Human Services Research Institute, University of Maine (http://tecathsri.org/shop_display_cart.asp?action=add&version=E-copy&id=9).

Reed, K.L. and Sanderson, S.N. (1992) *Concepts of occupational therapy* (3rd edn), Baltimore, MD: Williams and Wilkins.

Reeves, A. (1999) *Recovery: A holistic approach*, Gloucester: Handsell Publishing (www.workingtorecovery.co.uk/Default.aspx?tabid=1056&CategoryID=1&List=0&Level=1&ProductID=26).

Rethink (2005) *A socially inclusive mental health service for Stockport* (www.penninecare.nhs.uk/pen/new/documents/Social%20Inclusion%20in%20Stockport%20-%20Service%20ModelMay%202005.pdf).

Ridgeway, P.A. (2000) 'Re-storying psychiatric disability: learning from first person narrative accounts of recovery', *Psychiatric Rehabilitation Journal*, vol 24, no 4, pp 335–343.

Ridgway, P.A. and Press, A. (2004) *Assessing the recovery commitment of your mental health services: A user's guide to the Developing Recovery Enhancing Environments Measure (DREEM)* (UK ed, P. Allott), UK pilot version (Email: Mentalhealthrecovery@blueyonder.co.uk).

Roberts, G. (2000) 'Narrative and severe mental illness: what place do stories have in an evidence-based world?', *Advances in Psychiatric Treatment*, vol 6, pp 432-41.

Roberts, G. (2006) 'Understanding madness', in G. Roberts, S. Davenport, F. Holloway and T. Tattan (eds) *Enabling recovery: The principles and practice of rehabilitation psychiatry*, London: Gaskell, Chapter Seven.

Roberts, G. and Wolfson, P. (2006) 'New directions in rehabilitation: learning from the recovery movement', in G. Roberts, S. Davenport, F. Holloway and T. Tattan (eds) *Enabling Recovery: The principles and practice of rehabilitation psychiatry*, London: Gaskell, Chapter Two.

SAMHSA (Substance Abuse and Mental Health Services Administration) (2005) *National consensus statement on mental health recovery* (http://mentalhealth.samhsa.gov/publications/allpubs/sma05-4129/).

SCIE (Social Care Institute for Excellence) (2003) *Types and quality of knowledge in social care*, Knowledge Review 3 (www.scie.org.uk/publications/knowledgereviews/kr03.pdf).

Scottish Executive (2006a) *Delivering for mental health* (www.scotland.gov.uk/Publications/2006/11/30164829/0).

Scottish Executive (2006b) *Rights, relationships and recovery: The report of the National Review of Mental Health Nursing in Scotland* (www.scotland.gov.uk/Publications/2006/04/18164814/0).

Scottish Office (2005) *The same as you? A review of services for people with learning disabilities* (www.scotland.gov.uk/ldsr/docs/tsay-00.asp).

Sowers, W. (2007) 'Recovery: an opportunity to transcend our difference', *Psychiatric Services*, vol 58, no 1 (http://psychservices.psychiatryonline.org/cgi/content/full/58/1/5).

Topor, A. (2001) *Managing the contradictions: Recovery from severe mental disorders*, SSSW no 18, Stockholm: Department of Social Work, Stockholm University.

Turner-Crowson J. and Wallcraft, J. (2002) 'The recovery vision for mental health services and research: a British perspective', *Psychiatric Rehabilitation Journal*, vol 25, no 3 (www.bu.edu/cpr/repository/articles/turner-crowson2002.pdf).

Unzicker, R. (1989) 'On my own: a personal journey through madness and re-emergence', *Psychosocial Rehabilitation Journal*, vol 13, no 1, pp 71-7.

Wallcraft, J. (2005) 'Recovery from mental breakdown', in J. Tew (ed) *Social perspectives in mental health*, London: Jessica Kingsley Publishers, chapter 11.

Warner, R. (1994) *Recovery from schizophrenia: Psychiatry and political economy* (2nd edn), London: Routledge.

Watkins, P. (2007) *Recovery – a guide for mental health practitioners*, London: Churchill Livingstone/Elsevier.

Whitwell, D. (2005) *Recovery beyond psychiatry*, London: Free Association Books.

Wisconsin (1997) Blue Ribbon Commission on Mental Health (www.bu.edu/cpr/repository/documents/BlueRibbonComm.pdf).

Woodbridge, K. and Fulford, K.W.M. (2004) *Whose values? A workbook for values-based practice in mental health care*, London: The Sainsbury Centre for Mental Health.

Appendix 1

Sources and Resources for recovery and self-management
The Black Wellness Initiative (www.blackwellness.co.uk/index.html) is engaged in an ethnocentric assertiveness programme focused on wellness for public and human service planning, design, provision and evaluation in England and Wales.
Circles Network (www.circlesnetwork.org.uk/) is a national voluntary organisation that uses the tools of person-centred planning to facilitate inclusion in the community, principally through the setting up of circles of support and individual projects.
Recovery Devon (Partnerships in mental health recovery) (www.recoverydevon.co.uk).
In-Control (www.in-control.org.uk/) believes people who need support can control their own lives and be full citizens.
Keepwell (www.keepwell.co.nz/default.aspx?AspxAutoDetectCookieSupport=1).
Long-term Medical Conditions Alliance (LMCA) (www.lmca.org.uk).
Manic Depressive Fellowship self-help resources (www.mdf.org.uk, email smt@mdf.org.uk).
Mary Ellen Copeland (WRAP) (www.mentalhealthrecovery.com).
Mindful Employer Initiative (www.mindfulemployer.net/) is aimed at increasing awareness of mental health at work and providing support for businesses in recruiting and retaining staff.
National Empowerment Center (US) (www.power2u.org).
New Zealand Mental Health Commission (www.mhc.govt.nz, email info@mhc.govt.nz).
Ohio State (www.mh.state.oh.us/oper/outcomes/outcomes.index.html): guiding principles of the recovery model and outcomes.
Schizophrenia Self-management Project (Rethink) (www.rethink.org/recovery/).
Schizophrenia anonymous (www.schizophrenia.com/help/Schizanon.html).
Scottish Recovery Network (www.scottishrecovery.net).
Shery Mead (intentional peer support) (www.mentalhealthpeers.com).
Whole Life: a CSIP workstream hosted by Eastern Region at www.eastern.csip.org.uk/our-work/whole-life.html
Working to recovery – Ron Colman's training organisation (www.workingtorecovery.co.uk).

Appendix 2: Contacts for services given as examples of recovery in practice

Devon and Torbay
Laurie Davidson
Practice Development Manager
Devon Partnership NHS Trust
Wonford House Hospital
Dryden Rd
Exeter EX2 5AF
Tel: 01364 661 121
laurie.davidson@btopenworld.com

Hertfordshire
Graham Munn
Head of Centre for Mental Health Recovery
School of Social, Community and Health Studies
University of Hertfordshire
Room G166, CP Snow Building
College Lane
Hatfield, Hertfordshire, AL10 9AB
Administration Team tel: 01707 284951
g.munn@herts.ac.uk

Northamptonshire
Tim Crisp
Performance and Development Manager
c/o Changing Minds
Mobile X3
Park Campus
University of Northampton
Broughton Green Road
Northampton, NN2 7AL
Tel: 07917788318
timothy.crisp1@ntlworld.com

Powys
Derek Turner	or	Derek Turner
Development Worker		Green Gauge Consultancy
Powys Agency for Mental Health		Maesyfed
Antur Gwy		Penybont
Park Road		Llandrindod Wells
Builth Wells		Powys LD1 5UA
Powys LD2 3BA		Tel: 01597 851951
Tel: 01982 553178		info@thomas-shop.com
derek.turner@pavo.org.uk		www.maesyfed.co.uk

Scotland
Simon Bradstreet
Network Director
Scottish Recovery Network
Europa Building
450 Argyle St
Glasgow, Scotland G2 8LG
Tel: 0141 240 7790
info@scottishrecovery.net

Sefton Recovery Group Network (SRGN)
Karen Colligan
SRGN/MHJCT
Sefton PCT
First Floor, North Entrance
Burlington House
Crosby Road North
Waterloo L22 OQB
Tel/Text/IM 07800 914730 or 0151 920 3356
Recovemast@aol.com
www.seftonrecoverygroup.org.uk

South East London
Dr Mike Slade
South London and Maudsley NHS Foundation Trust
m.slade@iop.kcl.ac.uk

Stoke-on-Trent
Suzanne Withington
Joint Commissioning Manager
Joint Commissioning Unit
Stoke-on-Trent Primary Care Trust
Heron House
120 Grove Road
Fenton
Stoke-on-Trent ST4 4LX
Tel: 01782 298202
suzanne.withington@northstaffs.nhs.uk